Context Clues

Reading Comprehension Book
Reading Level 3.5–5.0

Introduction

Welcome to the Edupress Context Clues Reading Comprehension Book. This resource is an effective tool for instruction, practice, and evaluation of student understanding of how to use context clues. It includes ideas on how to introduce context clues to students, as well as activities to help teach and practice the concept.

The reproducible activities in this book are tailored to individual, small-group, and whole-class work. They include leveled reading passages, graphic organizers, worksheets, and detailed instruction pages. These activities provide opportunities to use text, illustrations, graphics, and combinations of these elements to practice using context clues to interpret text.

The material in this book is written for readers at the 3.5–5.0 reading level. However, the activities can easily be adapted to your students' ability levels and your time frame. After introducing an activity to students, model it by working through one or two examples aloud. You may wish to also read text passages aloud to students, or they can be read silently or aloud by students. For students who need personalized help, individual and small-group activities have been included. These activities can be done alone or with a classroom aide for explicit instruction.

We know you will be pleased with the progress your students make in using context clues after using this book.

Reproducible for classroom use only.
Not for use by an entire school or school system.

EP2367 © 2010 Demco, Inc. • 4810 Forest Run Road • Madison, WI 53704

ISBN 13: 978-1-56472-157-0

www.edupressinc.com

Table of Contents

Directions: Types of Context Clues

Whole Class/Individual 

Reproduce Types of Context Clues on page 4 for each student. As a class, review the four types of context clues and their examples. Then, review a text the class has read together. Model finding the meaning of a word by looking at context clues in the text, and identify the types of context clues you have used aloud. Then select words in the text, and have students identify the types of context clues that point to their meaning. Explain that sometimes a context clue can fit into more than one category.

Individual/Small Group 

Reproduce Identifying Types of Context Clues 1 and 2 on pages 5 and 6 for each student. Have students work individually or with partners to determine which type of context clue each sentence provides, writing the answer in the space next to the sentence. Have them underline the word or words in each sentence that helped them.

As an extension, challenge students to write their own sentences using the different types of context clues. Have them exchange with a partner, then underline the context clues in their partner's sentences and identify the types.

Answer Key

Identifying Types of Context Clues 1 (Page 5)

1. synonym
2. antonym
3. synonym
4. synonym/explanation
5. synonym
6. example
7. explanation
8. explanation
9. explanation
10. antonym
11. antonym

Identifying Types of Context Clues 2 (Page 6)

1. explanation
2. explanation
3. example
4. explanation
5. explanation
6. antonym
7. explanation
8. explanation
9. antonym
10. synonym

© Demco, Inc. 2010

Types of Context Clues

A context clue is a hint in a sentence. If you don't know the meaning of a word, look at the other words in the sentence or paragraph. They will give you hints about the word you don't know. Here are four common types of context clues that you will find in sentences:

Synonym:

A single word that has the same meaning is somewhere in the sentence or paragraph.

EXAMPLE

Justin was **furious** when his brother stole his allowance—I have never seen him so **angry**!

Antonym:

A single word that has the opposite meaning is somewhere in the sentence or paragraph.

EXAMPLE

My brothers often **argue** with each other, but my sisters **agree** on everything.

Explanation:

The word's meaning is explained with a phrase in the sentence or paragraph.

EXAMPLE

The **hurricane** was the **largest coastal storm** in five years.

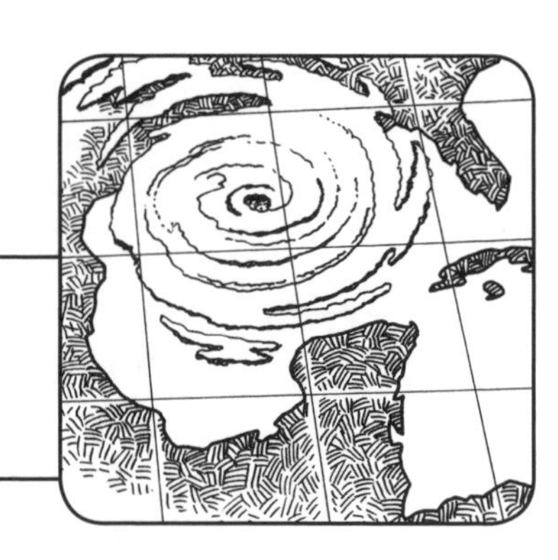

Example:

The word's meaning is given by an example or a list of examples in the sentence or paragraph.

EXAMPLE

Members of royalty, such as **kings**, **queens**, **and princes**, are treated with respect.

© Demco, Inc. 2010

Identifying Types of Context Clues 1

Name:______________________

Directions: Write which type of context clue helped you figure out each bold word. Then, underline the context clue in the sentence.

1. ______________________ If you don't eat this fruit soon, it will begin to **decay**, or rot.

2. ______________________ Brianna was **uncertain** about the question, but she gave her answer as though she was sure of it.

3. ______________________ We had **surplus** food after our camping trip, so we ate the extra meals at home.

4. ______________________ An army uniform has symbols on it. These **emblems** show what the person has done in the army.

5. ______________________ We passed our exit on the **turnpike** and had to drive on the highway for longer than we wanted to.

6. ______________________ **Violence**, whether it is hitting, kicking, or punching, is not tolerated at school.

7. ______________________ The farmer let the cows out in the **pasture**, where they could eat the grass that covered the ground.

8. ______________________ We had so much fun at the party! Everyone had a **terrific** time.

9. ______________________ Marcus **divided** the last piece of cake, and then he and his brother each took one part.

10. ______________________ Mr. James wants us to be **prompt** in the mornings, not late.

11. ______________________ Martina used to be **frail**, but in the past year, she has become strong.

© Demco, Inc. 2010

Identifying Types of Context Clues 2

Name:________________________

Directions: Write which type of context clue helped you figure out each bold word. Then, underline the context clue in the sentence.

1. ____________________ "I heard that it's supposed to rain tonight and tomorrow," Ryan said. "That's what the **forecast** on Channel 7 was."

2. ____________________ The new cafeteria has lots of room for many tables. It is much more **spacious** than the old lunchroom.

3. ____________________ Many of the city's **structures**, including houses, office buildings, and factories, were damaged from the flood.

4. ____________________ **Bamboo**, a fast-growing tropical plant, is the panda bear's favorite food.

5. ____________________ The **boundary** of the schoolyard is marked by a fence, which separates it from the house next door.

6. ____________________ Some smells **repel** mosquitoes, but other smells attract them.

7. ____________________ Evan does not **pause** between his sentences—he speaks so quickly that he becomes breathless!

8. ____________________ **Admission** to the fair is free—you don't have to pay to get in.

9. ____________________ Tia was **reluctant** to give her speech, but Jasmina was enthusiastic about talking in front of the class.

10. ____________________ We celebrated our win on the soccer field. We had a pizza party on the day of our **victory**.

© Demco, Inc. 2010

Directions: Building Vocabulary

Individual

Give one copy of "The Superhero Shopping Trip" on page 8 or "Fresh from the Field" on page 9 to each student, along with several copies of the Vocabulary Graphic Organizer on page 10. Ask students to complete the graphic organizer for each, or a set number, of the bold words in the story, using context clues and a dictionary to find the answers.

Small Group 

Divide the class into pairs. Reproduce "The Superhero Shopping Trip" or "Fresh from the Field" along with three copies of the Vocabulary Graphic Organizer for each pair. Have partners read the story aloud to each other and review the bold words. Then, have them work together to fill in the graphic organizer for three of the bold words. They can fill it in cooperatively, or have each student take one half of the organizer and write in the answers. Upon completion, the pairs should discuss and check one another's work.

Whole Class 

Choose one of the stories to reproduce for each student. Then, reproduce the graphic organizer on a transparency. Have students take turns reading the story aloud. Then, as a class, complete the graphic organizer for each word. Encourage students to identify and discuss the specific context clues that lead them to the meaning of the words.

© Demco, Inc. 2010

The Superhero Shopping Trip

"Let's see," Ezra said as he looked at the shopping list. "We need about 20 different items."

"Maybe we should get a cart," his mother said. "It will be easier to use one than to carry everything in our arms."

Ezra **selected** a cart from the line at the front **entrance**, and he and his mother made their way into the store. Ezra set the list on the cart seat and **steered** the cart toward the aisle that had a sign reading "School Supplies."

"Why don't we leave the cart in one spot? I'll **gather** the items I need a few at a time," he said to his mother. He pushed the cart to a corner and took the list.

"There certainly are a lot of people shopping for the same things we are," his mother **observed** as she looked at the other parents and kids in the aisle.

"What if there are no Steel Man folders and notebooks left?" Ezra **worried**. "I really want them, and I'm afraid they'll be gone."

"I'm sure the store ordered hundreds of Steel Man items," his mom **assured** him. "It was the most **popular** movie of the summer. They know that many kids will want to have Steel Man school supplies." Ezra felt better.

Ezra **consulted** the list. "I need three folders and notebooks," he said after studying the list. "Those are the first items listed."

His mom **offered** him a pen. "Why don't you cross each item off the list when you select it," she said, as she held out the pen.

Ezra took the pen and searched the shelves until he **discovered** the notebooks. He sighed with **relief** when he saw Steel Man on some of them. He chose three and then drew a line through the item on the list.

His mother waited patiently with the cart while Ezra **browsed** through the selection of folders, pencils, book covers, and pencil boxes. She looked **amused** as the cart filled up with Steel Man school supplies.

"Why are you smiling?" Ezra questioned her. "There's nothing funny about having to go back to school!"

"Oh, I know you're sorry about summer coming to an end," she said. "I just hope that by the time this school year ends, you're as **fond** of Steel Man as you are at this moment!"

Ezra nodded **enthusiastically**. "I will be," he told her. "It's not like all the other **phases** I went through. I liked Ant Man, then Gigantor, and then Wonder Man, but they weren't as **awesome** as Steel Man. Steel Man is the best!"

Ezra kept searching for Steel Man things. While he did so, he thought about what his mother had said. Then he **recalled** that in third grade, he had chosen all Gigantor school supplies. By Halloween, he had begged his mother to take him back to the store to **purchase** different folders and notebooks. All the kids were sick of their Gigantor stuff.

"Hmm," he **muttered** under his breath. He glanced back at the cart and saw the face of Steel Man staring back at him from about 20 **assorted** items, including folders, pencils, and notebooks.

Ezra looked at the lunch boxes. There was one with Steel Man on it. Ezra **considered** it for a moment. Then, he reached for the one next to it. It had bold black and red stripes on it with a silver handle. It wasn't a Steel Man lunch box, but he had a feeling that in several months, he would be glad it wasn't.

 © Demco, Inc. 2010

Fresh from the Field

Many cities and small towns have farmers' markets **throughout** the summer months. These weekly markets are like outdoor stores where people can **purchase** fresh fruits and vegetables. They can also buy other foods. People visit the markets because they want local, fresh food that has been grown at **nearby** farms.

Most farmers' markets have booths or carts. Each farmer comes to the market early to set up his or her booth. Some farmers grow many kinds of **produce**. That's a lot of fruits and vegetables to bring! That farmer might have helpers to **assist** with the booth.

Some farmers load up their trucks before dawn. They drive to the market in the dark. They set up their booths and make neat piles of tomatoes, beans, lettuce, carrots, and other delicious and **nutritious** foods that are good for you.

Some markets have not just a few, but **dozens,** of booths. Many of these farmers might have the same kinds of foods. For instance, sometimes every booth has tomatoes for sale. How does a farmer get a shopper to buy his or her tomatoes? Some offer lower prices than the farmer at the next booth. That way, they can make sure that they sell all their food while it is at its **peak**—fresh and ripe.

Depending on the time of year, you can find a **variety** of items at your local farmers' market. In early spring, you might **discover** piles of fresh spinach and lettuce. In midsummer, you will see big sacks of sweet corn. People buy the **cobs**, or ears, of corn by the dozen.

Tomatoes, peaches, and watermelons also are **typical** summer foods at the market. Because they have so much, many farmers cut up these foods and offer free **samples**. Then, people can taste them.

But people aren't the only ones who like these samples! Sometimes bees and hornets visit the farmers' markets, too. If a farmer gives you a sample of watermelon, be sure to check it. You wouldn't want to sample a bee!

Bees also might be curious about the honey booths. Some farmers keep honeybees and **collect** the honey to sell. These farmers put the honey in large and small **containers**. Sometimes, the honey is dark **amber**, and sometimes it is light yellow. It depends on the kind of flowers the bees visit before they make the honey. No matter what the color is, honey is another special treat you will find at the farmers' market.

Some farmers take their fruits and turn them into jam or jelly to sell at the market. Jam from the store is tasty, but these homemade fruit treats are even more **delicious**.

It's not always just food at the markets. Some farmers' markets have craft booths, too. People make things out of wood and fabric to sell. They build birdhouses and make decorations, such as wreaths and curtains. You might even find a booth that sells **jewelry**, such as rings and bracelets.

When you visit a farmers' market, you might come away with many things. You could **depart** with a bag of fresh, ripe tomatoes, or you might leave with a jar of strawberry jam. You might leave with a beautiful necklace. You might even go home with a full stomach from all the free samples!

© Demco, Inc. 2010

Name:____________________

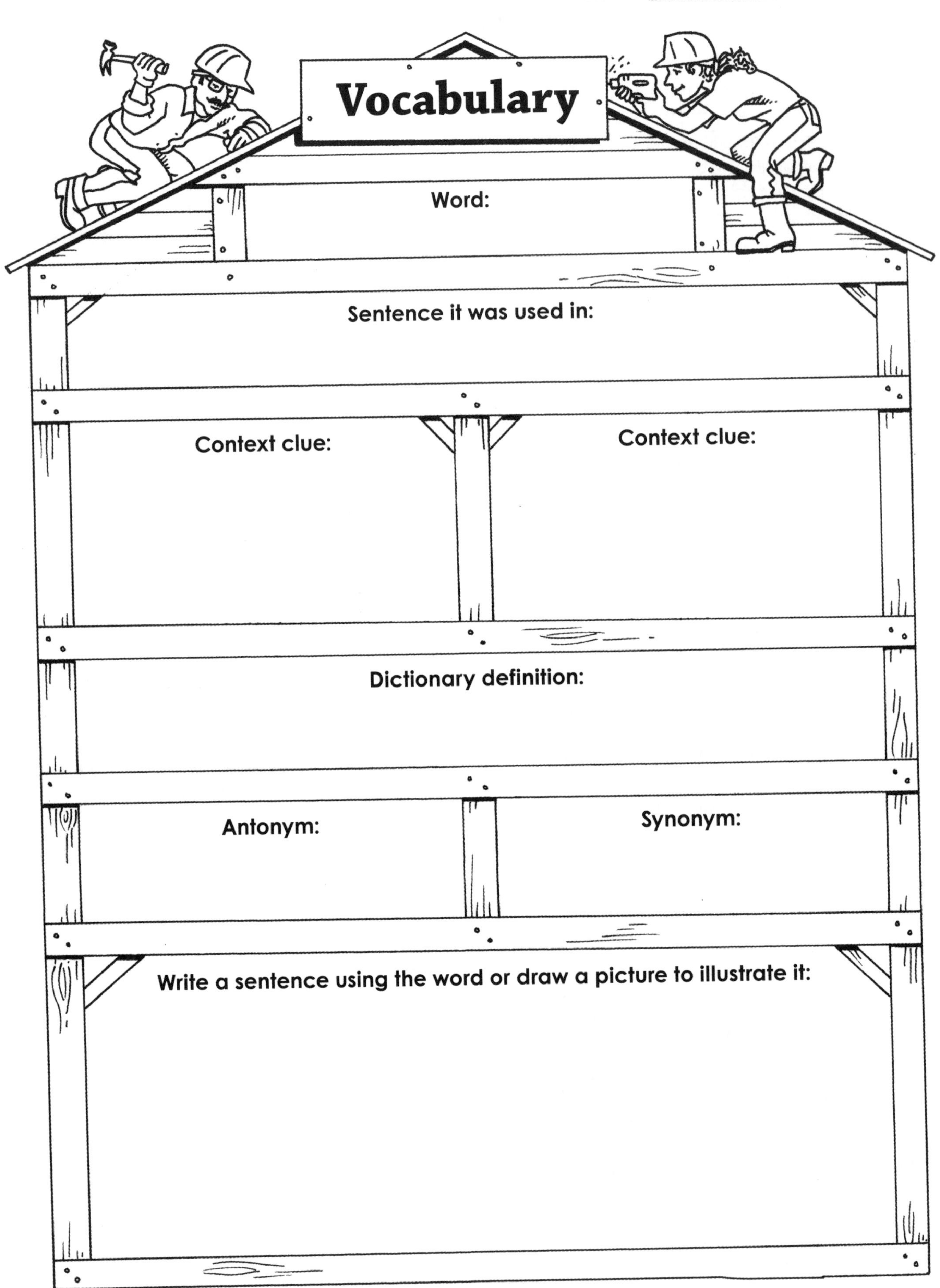

© Demco, Inc. 2010

Directions: Silly Sentences

Individual

Reproduce a Silly Sentences worksheet on page 12 or 13 for each student. Tell students to find and circle the word that doesn't fit in the context of each sentence and write an appropriate word underneath. Discuss the activity as a class, and explain that there might be more than one word that can replace the incorrect word.

Small Group

Make multiple copies of the Silly Sentence Cards on page 14, cut them apart, and give each student five cards. Ask students to write a sentence on each card. Four of the sentences should make sense, and the fifth should be a silly sentence with a word that doesn't fit. Divide the class into groups of five. In each group, have students take turns handing out their cards. Each student should read one aloud. The team should then decide which sentence contains a word that doesn't fit the context. The person holding that card is then challenged to state a word that fits correctly in the sentence.

For pairs of students, make multiple copies of the Silly Sentence Cards, cut them apart, and split them between the two students. Ask them to write their own silly sentences, using at least one word that does not fit in the context of each sentence. Have each student trade with a partner, and have the partner circle clues in each sentence that show which word is not contextually correct.

Whole Class

Use the Silly Sentence Cards to write several correct sentences and several that contain a word that does not fit the context. Put the cards in a bag. Divide the class into two teams, and have Team One pick a card from the bag and read the sentence out loud to Team Two. Team Two must then determine if the sentence is "silly" or "correct." If the team is right, they earn a point. If they can replace an incorrect word with a context-correct word, they earn another point. Play then passes to the other team and can continue until a desired point level is reached or until all sentences are used.

Answer Key (suggested answers)

Silly Sentences 1 (Page 12)

1. figure; thirteen
2. flower; planet
3. magnet; test
4. eyelids; plastic
5. clicking; talking
6. pencils; grass
7. banana; light
8. popcorn; leaves
9. microwave; frame
10. pine cone; ocean
11. haircuts; lightning
12. drive; understand

Silly Sentences 2 (Page 13)

1. dance; listen
2. magazines; motorcycles
3. find; do
4. books; meals
5. argued; asked
6. write; have
7. gargle; live
8. paintings; vegetables
9. minnow; window
10. running; staying
11. dentist; library
12. waffle; test

© Demco, Inc. 2010

Silly Sentences 1

Name:____________________

Directions: Circle the word that doesn't belong. Write the correct word below it.

1. There weren't always 50 states in the United States—in the beginning there were only figure colonies.

2. Rico and Patrick decided to do their science project on the flower Jupiter.

3. The local library is a good place to study for a magnet, because it is usually very quiet there.

4. Some dishes are made out of glass, some out of china, and some out of eyelids.

5. "Who were you clicking to on the telephone?" Aunt Edie asked Jeremy.

6. Once a week, my brother starts the lawnmower, and cuts all the pencils in the yard.

7. The eye doctor will look in your eyes with a very bright banana to see if they are healthy.

8. In autumn, we go out to the yard and rake all the red, yellow, and orange popcorn into big piles.

9. Mom loved the photograph we gave her, so she put it in a pretty microwave and hung it on the wall.

10. Did you ever take a vacation to the mountains or to the pine cone to watch the waves?

11. Count the seconds between the haircuts and the thunder to see how far away the storm is.

12. Maria and Max didn't drive the math homework, so they asked the teacher about it in the morning.

© Demco, Inc. 2010

Silly Sentences 2

Name:____________________

Directions: Circle the word that doesn't belong. Write the correct word below it.

1. More than 40 students crowded into the room to dance to Mr. Watson's speech.

2. There are many types of vehicles on the road, including cars, trucks, and magazines.

3. Firefighters have to be strong in order to find their job.

4. It's a good idea to eat three nutritious books a day, along with a healthy snack or two.

5. "How much money are you taking to the shopping mall?" Drew argued Mike.

6. Spiders write eight legs, but ants and other insects have six legs.

7. Some fish live in salt water, and some gargle in fresh water.

8. Broccoli and other bright, colorful paintings contain many vitamins.

9. Rose's little brother likes to watch the birds at the bird feeder through the minnow.

10. When we go on vacation, we usually take a tent and camp out instead of running at a hotel.

11. You can check out books, movies, and magazines at the dentist.

12. "Don't forget to study for your math waffle tonight," Dad said to Michael.

© Demco, Inc. 2010

Silly Sentence Cards

Name: ______________________________

© Demco, Inc. 2010

Directions: Silly Stories

Individual ●

Reproduce "Vacation Jitters" and "A Special Place" on pages 16 and 17 for each student. Use the first to model using context clues to figure out the missing words. Talk aloud, and model your thinking process as you read and identify the context clues. Students will then read and fill in the blanks of the second story. Ask them to underline the context clues that helped them guess the missing words.

Small Group

Pair up students. Reproduce "Vacation Jitters" and "A Special Place" for each pair and give each student a different story. This student will determine what part of speech the missing words are and then write the part of speech under the blank. Students may need guidance in this activity. Check to make sure they have written the correct part of speech. Then, without letting his or her partner see the story, the student should ask for a word that matches the part of speech for each blank in the story. After all the words are filled in, the other partner can read the silly version aloud. After the silly story is read, the partners can then discuss which words would fit in the blanks to make the story make sense. Then, have students switch roles.

Whole Class

Divide the class into two teams. Have each student write a sentence with a missing word. Tell students to include context clues in their sentences to allow others to guess the missing word. Have the first team read a sentence aloud or write it on the board and challenge the other team to come up with the missing word. Give a point for each correct word. Play then passes to the other team and can continue until a desired point level is reached or all sentences are used.

Answer Key

"Vacation Jitters" (Page 16)

asked
suitcase
sweater
swimming
pajamas
camera
sunglasses
rolled/wheeled/pulled
excited
watch
airplanes
parked
airport
nervous/worried

"A Special Place" (Page 17)

languages
long
people
dancers
skirts
beach
waves
water
board/feet
work
sweet
sleep/stay
meals
outside/outdoors
lava
hike/climb
picture

© Demco, Inc. 2010

Vacation Jitters

Name:__________________________

"What time does the plane take off?" Marie asked her mother.

Her mother laughed. "That's the third time you've ______________ me that question," she said. "Between you and your brother, I've answered it five times! It takes off at 3 o'clock."

Maria counted the hours. They had only two hours left to finish packing. She raced down the hall to her brother's room.

As Maria entered the room, she had to duck to avoid being hit by the sweater that Mario threw toward the suitcase.

"Why are you packing a sweater?" Maria asked. "It's not cold in Hawaii!"

"Well, what if the hotel room is cold?" Mario asked. He went over to the bed and folded the sweater, then he put it in his ______________.

Maria thought about this for a moment. Then she went to her room and opened a dresser drawer. She took out a warm, fuzzy ______________ and put it in her suitcase. She looked at the other items she had packed. There was a bathing suit to wear when she went ______________ in the ocean. There were several pairs of ______________ for sleeping. She had packed a ______________ because she wanted to have lots of pictures to show her friends. She had even remembered a pair of ______________ because she had heard the sun was very bright in Hawaii.

"It's time to put the suitcases in the car," Mom called to the kids.

Mario and Maria nearly ran into each other as they dragged their bags out into the hallway. Each suitcase had wheels, so they ______________ them down the hall to the back door.

Mom helped them load the bags into the car. Her suitcase was already there.

"Is it time to go?" Mario asked. He was so ______________ that he was grinning and jumping up and down.

Mom checked the ______________ on her wrist. "Almost," she said.

Finally, it was time to head to the airport. Neither Maria nor Mario had ever flown on an airplane before. As they approached the airport and saw the giant ______________ taking off and landing, the kids became nervous.

"Mom, what is flying like?" Mario asked. He sounded worried.

Mom found a parking place and ______________ the car. As she unloaded the suitcases, she explained what would happen inside the airport.

Mario and Maria listened quietly to their mother as they walked through the ______________. As they filled out the nametags for their bags, she told them what it was like to fly on an airplane.

Her explanation helped them relax. The kids no longer felt ______________.

"Never mind about the airplane trip," Maria said to her mother. "Tell us about Hawaii!"

© Demco, Inc. 2010

A Special Place

Name:_______________

The state flag of Hawaii has eight stripes. Each stripe represents one of the Hawaiian islands. It is the only state that is made up of islands—and that makes it a very special place.

What makes Hawaii so special? Lots of things! For instance, many people on the islands speak two ______________: English and Hawaiian. The Hawaiian language has some very long words—one kind of fish has a name that is 16 letters ______________!

In addition to having their own language, Hawaiian ______________ are unique in other ways. They have a special dance called the hula. Hula ______________ use the movements of the dance to tell a story. Each motion tells the audience something. The dancers wear special costumes, including grass ______________ and flower necklaces.

Sometimes, the dancers perform at a special party, called a luau. Music, dancing, and certain foods are part of the fun at this kind of event. Often, the parties take place at night on the sandy ______________. When the music stops, people can hear the ______________ crashing on the beach.

But Hawaiian people don't just listen to the ocean waves. They like to get out in the salt ______________ and surf. Surfing is a very popular sport in Hawaii. If you go surfing, you will use a board that is about as tall as an adult. You take the board into the water and then lie down on it. You paddle out and wait for a high wave and stand up on your ______________. You travel along the wave until you fall or until the wave goes away. If you want to become a great surfer, you will have to practice for many hours.

Surfing and dancing are fun, but Hawaiian people also ______________ hard at their jobs. Many people are farmers in Hawaii. They grow fruits, such as pineapple, and sugar cane. Much of the sugar you see in your grocery store comes from this plant. Hawaiian sugar is used in candy, cookies, and cakes, too. The ______________ taste of sugar is hard to resist!

Some Hawaiian people work to help visitors to the islands. Because the islands are so pretty, people come from all over the world to see their beauty. The visitors ______________ in hotels, and they eat their ______________ in restaurants. Workers in these places do their jobs indoors, but many Hawaiians work ______________, too. Some take people on boat rides. Some show visitors how to surf. Some take groups to see beautiful waterfalls and rain forests. Some even show visitors volcanoes.

Hawaii is famous for having many volcanoes. These hollow mountains are filled with hot ______________, or melted rocks. Some volcanoes are safe to visit, so Hawaiians lead hikes to the tops, which might seem like a strange job. If you visit Hawaii, you might be able to ______________ all the way up to the mouth of a volcano. If you do this, be sure to have someone take your ______________ with a camera so you can show it to all your friends at home!

© Demco, Inc. 2010

Directions: What Is the Meaning of This?

Individual ●

Reproduce "The Perfect Party Plan" on page 19 and "Is It Magic?" on page 21 and their matching vocabulary worksheets on pages 20 and 22 for each student. Have students read one story, circling the words throughout that give clues to the meanings of the unfamiliar bold words. They can then use the vocabulary worksheet to write down what they believe each word means.

Before students read the next story, ask them to fill in any definitions on the list they think they already know. After they read the story, ask them to assess these definitions and to write definitions for the other words. When all students have finished, ask students to share their definitions. How many did they already know? How many did they figure out from reading the story?

Small Group ●●

Divide students into pairs. Reproduce either "The Perfect Party Plan" or "Is It Magic?" along with two matching vocabulary worksheets for each pair. After they read the story aloud together, have students individually write down what they think each bold word means. When they are finished, have partners exchange their lists, then look up the words in dictionaries. They should circle the correct definitions on their partners' lists and compare their answers afterward.

Whole Class 

Reproduce one of the stories along with its matching vocabulary worksheet for each student. Have each student read the story and write definitions for the words on the list. When students are finished, read the correct definitions aloud, asking students to circle the words they got correct. When all the definitions are read, collect the lists and graph on the board how many students got one, two, three, etc., correct. Then discuss the results. Were the words most students got correct ones they were already familiar with?

© Demco, Inc. 2010

The Perfect Party Plan

Emma was **stumped**. She had been thinking for hours about her next birthday party, and she couldn't decide on a theme.

Her friends always looked forward to her birthday celebrations. Emma's parents spent days planning the events. However, this year, Emma was on her own. Her parents had given her **sole** responsibility—now she was in charge. She didn't want to let her friends down—she had to come up with a great party idea!

Emma stared at the list of her past parties. "Let's see," she **mused** aloud. The list she had written was supposed to help her think.

For her fifth birthday, the theme had been simple. It was a painting party, and all her friends had helped create a **mural** on her bedroom walls. The painting had **depicted** a fairy tale world. The mural even showed a castle surrounded by a **moat**. Emma remembered painting the water in the moat with her friend Alyssa.

Of course, Emma had outgrown the fairy tale room years ago. Now, her room was painted in a more grown-up style.

She looked at another party on the list. When she was seven, she'd had a carnival party.

"That was fun," Emma **recalled**. She remembered that the kids had played games, eaten snow cones, and jumped in a bouncy house. Emma had given out play money. She had a ticket booth where her guests "bought" tickets to play games. They also used the fake money to buy popcorn, snow cones, and other carnival food.

Emma laughed as she remembered the most popular part of the carnival—the petting zoo. She had borrowed a **diverse** group of pets from family and friends. The zoo consisted of a ferret, a dog, a kitten, a lizard, and a bowl of goldfish. The fish actually had two **purposes**: they were part of the zoo, and they were used as carnival prizes.

"We didn't get to pet them because they were in water," she thought with a laugh. "However, they did make good prizes."

The last party on her list was the most recent. Last year, she had a party with a rain forest theme. She had filled the house with tropical decorations, such as palm trees, colorful flowers, and coconuts. The **refreshments** were tropical, too. She had served pineapple drinks and fruit salad. She played Hawaiian music, and the guests danced until they were so **fatigued** they all had to rest.

"That was a lot of fun," Emma said to herself. "But what am I going to do this year?" She was getting **discouraged**. She doubted she would ever be able to top her other parties.

Finally, she had an idea. She ran to the computer to search the Internet. There had to be some party theme sites. Emma was certain she would find the answer to her problem.

As she turned on the computer, she wondered how the Internet worked. It seemed strange that you could type words into it and suddenly have thousands of answers to your **dilemma**. "It's almost like magic," she thought. Suddenly, her mouth fell open. "That's it! I'll have a magic party! We can watch a magician. Maybe we can even learn how the tricks work, and do some ourselves!"

Emma felt **elated**. She was so excited—she had thought of the perfect party plan.

© Demco, Inc. 2010

Vocabulary for "The Perfect Party Plan"

Name: ______________________

stumped ______________________

sole ______________________

mused ______________________

mural ______________________

depicted ______________________

moat ______________________

recalled ______________________

diverse ______________________

purposes ______________________

refreshments ______________________

fatigued ______________________

discouraged ______________________

dilemma ______________________

elated ______________________

© Demco, Inc. 2010

Is It Magic?

Have you ever been to a party where a magician performed? Did the magician pull a rabbit from an empty hat? Did the magician make an object **vanish**, then reappear? A magician can even make a person disappear, then reappear somewhere else. At the end of the show, were you left wondering how these tricks worked?

A magician's act is filled with mysterious tricks that look magical, but in reality, these performers don't **rely** on magic. They depend on **illusion**. This means they fool you into thinking you saw something you really did not.

When you **witness** a magic trick, what you don't see is just as important as what you do see. Magicians have to **distract** you from seeing how they really do their tricks. They try to direct your attention to something else while they do the work that makes the magic trick appear real.

A magician must use **misdirection**, or draw your attention away from what is happening. Misdirection is a **vital** part of any magician's act. The magician could not do the trick without it.

How do magicians distract their audiences? If you watch an **amateur** magician perform, you might get your answer. Unlike professional magicians, amateurs have not had much practice. If you watch them carefully, you might see how their tricks work.

A magician might get the audience to look at a different part of the stage or a member of the audience instead of her. While you are looking in a different direction, she can then do the trick. By the time you look back, the "magic" has already happened. A good magician uses misdirection in a **subtle** way. She doesn't make a big fuss so that the audience looks somewhere else. She might just move her left hand around. Then, while you are looking at her left hand, she does the trick with her right hand.

Some magic shows use special effects, such as lights, smoke, and music, to distract the audience. For these, the magician needs an **assistant**. This helper will turn on the lights, music, and smoke machines at just the right moments, when the magician wants the audience to be distracted.

Other magicians will get the audience to pay attention to what they are saying instead of what they are doing. Some magicians use comedy to distract. It might sound like the magician just thought of these jokes or stories, but they have practiced them until they can **recite** them perfectly.

All of these ways to **divert** your attention take practice. Of course, it also takes a lot of time to become really good at magic tricks. Magicians **rehearse** for many hours until they are good at each trick. Many magicians like to practice in front of mirrors so they can see what the audience will see.

Many magic tricks make objects seem to appear or disappear. Sometimes, the object is as small as a coin, and sometimes it is as large as a person. Magicians have to move these objects without you knowing. If you watch closely you might notice when the "magic" happens, but you will have to pay close **attention**!

© Demco, Inc. 2010

Vocabulary for "Is It Magic?"

Name: ____________________

vanish ____________________

____

rely ____________________

____

illusion ____________________

____

witness ____________________

____

distract ____________________

____

misdirection ____________________

____

vital ____________________

____

amateur ____________________

____

subtle ____________________

____

assistant ____________________

____

recite ____________________

____

divert ____________________

____

rehearse ____________________

____

attention ____________________

____

© Demco, Inc. 2010

Directions: Made-Up Words

Individual ●

Reproduce "The Sport of Karate" on page 24 or "Lessons Learned" on page 25 for each student. Ask students to read the story and circle the words they think are made up. On another sheet of paper, have them write each suspect word, then a real word that they think might take its place. Then, have them highlight or underline the context clues in the story that helped them figure out the real words. As a class, discuss the made-up words and what they might mean.

Small Group ●●

Have students write their own stories, then go through and replace several real words with made-up ones. Ask them to exchange their stories with a partner. Have partners read the new stories, circle the words they think are made up, and replace them with appropriate words. Then, have students discuss with their partner why they chose these new words.

Whole Class ●●●

Using the answer key below, make a list on the board, out of order, of words that can replace the made-up words in one of the stories. Then, reproduce the story on a transparency. Read the story aloud to the class. As you read, ask students to raise their hands or stand up if they hear a word they think is made up. Circle the words on the transparency as students identify them. After you've finished reading the story, go through the story and read the sentences with made-up words in them. Challenge students to be the first to find a word from the list on the board to replace the made-up word and shout it out. Ask the other students if they agree. Write the correct word on the transparency.

Answer Key (suggested answers)

"The Sport of Karate" (Page 24)

trippo = world
wede = feet
martle = practice/learn
feepor = teach
lenax = learn
arterms = friends
heppy = help/teach
seckles = lessons
porge = uniform
gemter = pass
freg = earn/get
boda = pay
peddering = learning
stull = keep
tremm = sport

"Lessons Learned" (Page 25)

reper = open
moaser = waist
triggit = down
mentles = minutes
treggled = said
galotting = practicing
browlly = stupid/silly
overps = fun/interesting
heskined = asked
mainted = pointed
dresture = different
certer = door
nonset = minute/second
ister = house
frelmed = undid/unbuckled
flends = lessons

© Demco, Inc. 2010

The Sport of Karate

Karate is a popular sport—many people participate in it. It is one of the martial arts, along with judo and kickboxing. In these sports, people fight each other, but they don't fight because they are angry. They are simply showing their skills at hitting and defending against hits.

Karate is a very old sport. It comes from the eastern part of the trippo and has changed over the centuries. Basically, its name means "empty hand." When you fight in karate, you use your bare hands to hit and block and your bare wede to kick and block.

If you are going to learn karate, you have to take your lessons seriously. Most people take karate because they think it will be fun, and they are correct. It is fun to martle this sport. However, you have to concentrate on what you are doing because if you are not careful, you could injure yourself or your partner.

Karate coaches have spent years learning the sport and more years learning how to feepor it to students. Sometimes, their classes have beginners and experts all together. As you might imagine, the beginners learn a lot from both the coach and from the experts in class. It's a great way to lenax quickly.

Some kids join karate classes because their friends are in them. However, class is not the place to have a conversation with your arterms. You are there to work, and the coach is there to heppy you. If you distract other learners with your noise, you will get into trouble. The coach might even make you leave the class. That would not only be embarrassing, but you would miss out on the rest of the lesson. These seckles are not free, so you are wasting money and time if you goof around in class.

One of the first things you will do in karate is order a porge. Usually, the uniform is a white shirt and pants. If you are a beginner, you will tie your shirt with a white belt. As you learn more about karate, you will take tests to earn belts of different colors. For example, if you gemter your first test, you will earn a belt with a yellow stripe or a solid yellow belt. After many years of studying and fighting, you can freg a brown belt or even a black belt. But you must have patience and dedication to make it that far in the sport of karate. You have to boda attention in class and practice at home.

Sometimes, you might get upset if you are having trouble peddering some of the moves. You might even go for a test and not get your next belt. If that happens, just remember that everyone has trouble. Even your coach struggled at times. The important thing is to stull trying!

In addition to learning an interesting tremm, you will be getting exercise. You will have better balance. You will have more confidence and self-control. You will be more polite and respectful to adults. If you dedicate yourself to karate, you might find that the lessons you learn in class help you in other parts of your life.

© Demco, Inc. 2010

Lessons Learned

"Hurry up!" Dad called up the stairs. "All three of you are going to be late for your lessons!"

Suddenly, three bedroom doors flew reper, and Tory, Drew, and Lily all rushed to the staircase.

Tory was holding a helmet, Drew had a music book in his hand, and Lily was tying a green belt around her moaser.

Dad waited impatiently while the kids raced triggit the stairs. "Let's go," he urged.

Finally, everyone was in the car with their seat belts on. Dad took off down the street.

"Who gets dropped off first?" Lily asked as she brushed a piece of dirt off her white karate uniform.

"You," Dad replied. "Your karate lesson starts in 20 mentles. What are you doing in class today?"

Lily tried to remember what the coach had demonstrated last week. "Well, I think we're going to work on our side kicks and front kicks."

"That doesn't sound like any fun at all," Drew treggled. "Today in my piano lesson, I am going to work on my scales. I've been galotting all week, and I can't wait to hear what the teacher says because I've really improved!"

Tory laughed at her brother and sister. They always argued about what was more fun: playing piano or doing karate. She thought it was a browlly argument. Couldn't they understand that learning how to ride a horse was much more overps than either of those activities?

"What's so funny, Tory?" Dad heskined.

"I'm so excited about my lesson today that I can't wait!" Tory burst out. "Who would want to bang on a piano or practice kicking when they could learn how to control a huge horse? I'm doing so well that the instructor says I'll be ready to jump over hurdles soon."

Drew mainted to the helmet in Tory's lap. "At least with piano lessons, you don't need to wear a stupid helmet!" Then he looked at Lily's uniform. "And you don't wear white pajamas, either!"

Both of the girls frowned at Drew.

"That's enough," Dad warned. "Just because you like dresture things doesn't mean that you can pester each other."

They had arrived at the gym where Lily took karate, so she hopped out of the car and bowed to her father, just like she bowed to her instructor in class.

"Thanks for the ride!" she said and ran into the building.

Next, they went to the stables where Tory took her riding lessons. She opened the car certer and grinned at her dad.

"Thanks," she said. Then she looked at Drew. "Have fun at your lesson. I hope you do well on your scales."

Drew looked surprised. "Good luck," he told her. "I hope your horse behaves."

Dad laughed and drove away. "You'll be right on time for your piano lesson," he assured Drew.

"Good," Drew sighed. "I don't want to waste a nonset!"

When they got to the ister where his music teacher lived, Drew frelmed his seat belt.

"Hey, Dad," he said. "I have a question. Why don't you take any lessons?"

Dad smiled. "A long time ago, I took some very important lessons," he replied.

"Oh, did you?" Drew said. "What kind of flends were they?"

"Driving lessons!" Dad said, chuckling. "I learned to drive a car, and now I use what I learned to take you kids all over town!"

© Demco, Inc. 2010

Directions: Multiple-Meaning Words

Individual

Reproduce Multiple-Meaning Words 1 and 2 on pages 27 and 28 for each student. Have students read the sentence groups and circle the letters of the two sentences that use the word in the same way. Then, have students choose one of the words and illustrate both of its meanings on the side of the page.

Also, reproduce Homonym Multiple Choice on page 30 for each student. Explain that homonyms are words that sound the same but are spelled differently and have different meanings. Have students circle the correct word for each sentence.

As an extension, have students use the Multiple-Meaning Word Cards on page 29 to write two sentences, one for each meaning of the word. Or, challenge them to write sentences that use both meanings of each word in the same sentence.

Small Group

Reproduce the Multiple-Meaning Word Cards for each student. Have each student choose five words from the list and write a one-page story using them. Divide students into groups of three or four, and have them read their stories aloud. Ask them to discuss how they got the ideas for their stories (this develops the skills of using prior knowledge and connecting text to self). Ask them to discover if others in their group chose the same words but used them with their different meanings.

Whole Class

Divide the class into two teams. Reproduce the Multiple-Meaning Word Cards and separate them into two groups. Give each team one group of words. Have each team write a sentence on a strip of paper for each of their words. Have the first team read a sentence out loud. The other team then states the multiple-meaning word and the definition of that word. If they are correct, they get a point. Play passes to the other team. Play until all words have been used. A bonus round can be done by repeating the multiple-meaning words and having teams shout out a second meaning for the word, with the first team to get the answer receiving the point.

Or, divide the class into two teams. Call out one of the multiple-meaning words. Have each student secretly draw the meaning of the word you've called out. At the end of a time limit, have teams compare papers. Count how many students on each team had similar drawings.

Answer Key

Multiple-Meaning Words 1 (Page 27)

1. b, c
2. a, c
3. b, c
4. a, c

Multiple-Meaning Words 2 (Page 28)

1. a, c
2. b, c
3. a, b
4. b, c

Homonym Multiple Choice (Page 30)

1. a
2. b
3. a
4. b
5. a
6. b
7. b
8. a
9. a
10. a
11. a
12. b
13. a

© Demco, Inc. 2010

Multiple-Meaning Words 1

Name:

Directions: In each set, circle the letters of the two sentences that use the same meaning of the bold word. Then, choose one of the sets of words and illustrate its two different meanings.

1

a "Don't shout while Aunt Mabel is napping," Mother said. "You might **alarm** her."

b The fire **alarm** at school is so loud that you can hear it from across the street.

c The police were called to the hardware store because someone set the **alarm** off.

2

a Did Kathy like the **present** that Jessie got her for her thirteenth birthday?

b When everyone was **present** and ready to go, the bus finally left for the field trip.

c I think it's just as much fun to shop for a **present** as it is to receive one.

3

a Gordy paid for the toy car with a 20-dollar **bill**.

b When my dad got the phone **bill** for July, he was upset about the amount of money he owed.

c After dinner at the restaurant, Granddad insisted on paying the **bill**.

4

a The sunflower has a giant, heavy bloom, so it needs a strong **stalk** to support it.

b The lion can **stalk** its prey over many miles.

c Each of the flowers grows on a separate **stalk**.

Meaning 1

Meaning 2

© Demco, Inc. 2010

Multiple-Meaning Words 2

Name:____________________

Directions: In each set, circle the letters of the two sentences that use the same meaning of the bold word. Then, choose one of the sets of words and illustrate its two different meanings.

1

a "It's not **fair**!" Isabelle shouted. "I want to go to the carnival!"

b We traveled for three hours to visit the state **fair**.

c Annie was angry that her mom had grounded her, but she knew the punishment was **fair**.

2

a The skateboarders always **coast** down this part of the sidewalk because it is downhill.

b The houses along the **coast** were damaged from the storm.

c If you go for a drive along the **coast**, you might see dolphins playing in the ocean.

3

a "What kind of doughnut do you like best?" Molly asked. "I prefer **plain** because I don't like sprinkles."

b The house was very **plain**—there were hardly any decorations at all.

c When you travel through a **plain**, you will see lots of tall grass and very few trees.

4

a My dad likes to **plan** our vacations down to the last minute.

b Did you look at the **plan** for the treehouse that Hector is building?

c I had a **plan** for a practical joke, but I decided not to do it after all.

Meaning 1

Meaning 2

© Demco, Inc. 2010

Multiple-Meaning Word Cards

goal	value	hammer
arch	trace	stamp
state	act	creep
burn	shape	track
peer	rate	grave
mold	support	brilliant
bright	check	light

© Demco, Inc. 2010

Homonym Multiple Choice

Name: ____________________

Directions: Choose the word that best fits each blank in the sentences below.

1. The bottom _____ was broken, so Mr. Gonzales put up a sign that said, "Please use the elevator."

   a) stair b) stare

2. Many butterflies have _____ colorful wings with interesting patterns.

   a) vary b) very

3. Evan was excited because he got the lead _____ in the school play.

   a) role b) roll

4. We decided to choose a _____ puppy because we already have a female cat.

   a) mail b) male

5. The _____ character in the book *Little House on the Prairie* is a girl named Laura.

   a) main b) mane

6. The _____ wolf lives by itself, away from the members of the pack.

   a) loan b) lone

7. We watch the show *Amazing People* because each person on it performs an incredible _____.

   a) feet b) feat

8. If the actor forgets his line, he will usually _____ until he remembers what to say.

   a) pause b) paws

9. Did you _____ that the starling is not a native bird to America?

   a) know b) no

10. The man walked with a peculiar _____, so we always recognized him from down the street.

    a) gait b) gate

11. The _____ landed on the longest runway at the airport.

    a) plane b) plain

12. Granddad couldn't believe how much the kids had _____ since he'd last seen them.

    a) groan b) grown

13. "The pain will _____ over the next few days as the burn begins to heal," the doctor said.

    a) lessen b) lesson

© Demco, Inc. 2010

Directions: Nonsense Words

Individual

Reproduce the Nonsense Word Cards on page 32 for each student. Ask each student to come up with a definition for each word, then to use it in a sentence. On separate sheets of paper, have students illustrate the definitions for three words. Students will draw on their prior knowledge, vocabulary, and knowledge of word origins to come up with definitions. Discuss with them how they chose certain definitions for words.

Small Group

Have students exchange one or two of their drawings from the Individual activity with a partner (make sure they've written the nonsense word at the top). Have partners write down what they think the meaning of the nonsense word is based on the drawing. Have partners reveal, compare, and discuss the made-up definitions. Were they correct in their guesses? What things in the drawings made them guess the definitions that they did? Alternatively, have students trade their sentences with partners. Have partners try to guess the meanings of the words using context clues from the sentences. If their definitions were similar, ask them to discuss what made them think of that meaning. Did the word look like another word? Did it sound like another word? If the partners' definitions weren't similar, did they choose to use the words in the same manner (i.e., nouns, verbs, etc.)?

Whole Class 

Reproduce the Nonsense Word Cards and cut them apart. Put the words in a bag. Divide the class into two teams. Have one student from each team draw a card. They each have 30 seconds to write a sentence using their nonsense words on the board. When the time is up, their team must guess the meaning of the word using context clues from their sentence. If the team is correct, they earn a point. If the team is stumped, they can guess if the word is being used as a noun, verb, etc., for a half point. The team with the most points at the end wins.

© Demco, Inc. 2010

Nonsense Word Cards

carasha	fubble
marf	unpepple
rotist	flatable
repouch	sklear
farb	contople
kaliscious	buttersnill
mindgrip	glup
sunister	discrown
cradnuckle	botherful
saltillion	gleg

© Demco, Inc. 2010

Directions: What's the Word?

Individual

Reproduce What's the Word? 1 and 2 on pages 34 and 35 for each student. Have students use context clues to fill in the missing words. Ask them to underline the clues in each sentence that led them to the correct answer. When all students are finished, discuss the answers as a class. Some sentences might have more than one correct word. Discuss the reasons students chose the words they did.

Small Group

Divide students into pairs. Ask them each to write five sentences with missing words. (They might find it easier to write complete sentences, then choose a word that is surrounded by context clues and remove that word.) Then, have students exchange papers with their partners and fill in the missing words. Students can then discuss the results with their partners.

Whole Class

Reproduce the What's the Word? pages on transparencies. Divide the class into two teams. Show one sentence at a time and ask one member from each team to call out a word that fits in the blank as quickly as they can. Teams are awarded a point each time a member calls out a correct answer first.

Answer Key (suggested answers)

What's the Word? 1 (Page 34)

1. moody
2. foggy
3. night
4. works
5. big
6. band
7. asked
8. garden
9. erased
10. pet
11. nervous
12. cleaned

What's the Word? 2 (Page 35)

1. best
2. class
3. pool
4. shopping
5. marshmallows
6. first
7. play
8. sports
9. bought
10. aunt
11. patterns
12. dark

© Demco, Inc. 2010

What's the Word? 1

Name:____________________

Directions: Use context clues to fill in the missing word in each sentence.

1. My sister Kellie is very ________________. One day she is happy, but the next she is angry or sad.
2. On mornings when the weather is ________________, we can't see very far through the mist.
3. Jasmine is having two friends over on Friday evening, and they will stay all ________________ long.
4. Jacob's mom is a nurse, and she ________________ at the hospital in the emergency room.
5. Your puppy is tiny now, but in a year or so, you will not believe how ________________ he has gotten.
6. There were four members in the ________________: two played guitar, one played bass, and one played drums.
7. "Have you ever been horseback riding?" Allen ____________ Laura.
8. Last year, we grew potatoes, corn, and green beans in our ________________ .
9. When Ms. Deitz finished the vocabulary lesson, she ________________ the words from the board and then wrote a math problem on it.
10. We went to the ________________ store and looked at the fish, the turtles, and the kittens that were for sale.
11. James is ________________, or scared, when he has to speak in front of the whole class.
12. My room was so messy that my mom grounded me until I ________________ up the entire mess.

© Demco, Inc. 2010

What's the Word? 2

Name: ____________________

Directions: Use context clues to fill in the missing word in each sentence.

1. Yellow, green, and red are Kellie's favorite colors, but Cheyenne likes blue, purple, and orange the ________________.

2. Everyone gasped with surprise when Mr. James revealed the new ________________ pet—a snake named Rufus.

3. Devin dove into the swimming ________________, where all her friends were already swimming.

4. When my parents take me grocery ________________, they ask me to pick out fresh fruits and vegetables.

5. We roasted ________________ over the campfire to make s'mores.

6. Some little kids are frightened when they go to the barbershop for their very ________________ haircut.

7. After three years of piano lessons, Jake is finally comfortable when he has to ________________ music in public.

8. Basketball, soccer, and volleyball are three ________________ that are played by teams instead of individuals.

9. My mom took me to a bookshop over the weekend, and I ________________ three books, which I will read this week.

10. My ________________, Marie, is my mother's sister.

11. Stripes, polka dots, and plaid are common ________________, or designs, for clothing.

12. The lights went out during the thunderstorm, so we sat in the ________________ for an hour.

© Demco, Inc. 2010

Directions: Using Antonyms and Synonyms as Context Clues

Individual ●

Discuss synonyms and antonyms with the class. Reproduce Antonyms and Synonyms Context Clues 1 and 2 on pages 37 and 38 for each student. Have students read the sentences and then circle the antonym or synonym that gives the context clue for the definition of the bold word. Have them write an "S" or an "A" above to show whether it is a synonym or antonym. Discuss the answers as a class.

Small Group ●●

Divide students into pairs. Reproduce Synonym/Antonym Cards 1 and 2 on pages 39 and 40 for each pair and cut them apart. Put the cards in a bag, and have each student pull a card out of the bag. Students can then use the word to write a sentence that gives context clues to its meaning through a synonym or antonym (allow them to use a dictionary or thesaurus if they need help). Rotate through groups to make sure students are using their words correctly. Have them underline their words in their sentences and exchange with partners. Partners try to figure out the meaning of the underlined word. If they get it right, they earn a point. Play continues until the set time is up or the pairs use all the words.

Whole Class 

Reproduce two sets of Synonym/Antonym Cards 1 and 2. Divide the class into two teams. Give each team member a card. Have students use the word to write a sentence that gives context clues to its meaning through a synonym or antonym. Students take turns stating their words and reading their sentences to their teammates. Teammates guess the meaning of the word. If they get it right, the team gets a point. Bonus points can be earned if the students correctly identify the synonym or antonym that provides the context clue for each word. The team with the most points at the end wins the game.

Answer Key

Antonyms and Synonyms Context Clues 1 (Page 37)

1. antonym, refused
2. antonym, scarce
3. synonym, fake
4. synonym, climb
5. antonym, sharp
6. antonym, stupid
7. synonym, hid
8. antonym, rude
9. synonym, gloom
10. antonym, unknown
11. synonym, huge
12. antonym, bold
13. antonym, gather
14. antonym, occupied
15. synonym, sunrise

Antonyms and Synonyms Context Clues 2 (Page 38)

1. antonym, defeat
2. antonym, freedom
3. synonym, cheap
4. antonym, frequent
5. antonym, generous
6. synonym, brave
7. antonym, wrong
8. antonym, calm
9. antonym, hope
10. synonym, fat
11. synonym, style
12. antonym, slowly
13. synonym, stay
14. synonym, hurt
15. synonym, lawyer

 © Demco, Inc. 2010

Antonyms and Synonyms Context Clues 1

Name:____________________

Directions: Circle the antonym or synonym that helps you understand the meaning of the bold word. Write an "S" or an "A" to show if it is an antonym or a synonym for the bold word.

1. The twins were having trouble with their homework. Andy **accepted** help, but Annie refused it.
2. In the summer, fresh fruit is **abundant**, but in the winter, it becomes more scarce.
3. This recipe calls for **artificial**, or fake, sweetener.
4. When the campers **ascend** the mountain, they will find the climb exhausting.
5. "This knife is too **blunt** to cut the steak," Hannah said. "Give me a sharp one."
6. We thought our joke was **clever**, but Dad thought it was stupid.
7. Maria **concealed** her report card from her parents. She hid it in her backpack.
8. Jenny is always **courteous** to her grandparents, but her cousins are sometimes rude.
9. The rain made the day seem **dismal**, but we tried to have fun in spite of the gloom.
10. Molly wants to be **famous**, but right now she is still unknown.
11. Until you see it, you have no idea how **immense** the mountain is. It is so huge!
12. My puppy used to be **timid** around strangers, but now she is bold.
13. Food pantries gather groceries and then **distribute** them to needy families.
14. On the way to school, the seat next to me was **vacant**. But on the way home, it was occupied.
15. I like to get up at **dawn** because I think sunrise is the prettiest time of day.

© Demco, Inc. 2010

Antonyms and Synonyms Context Clues 2

Name:____________________

Directions: Circle the antonym or synonym that helps you understand the meaning of the bold word. Write an "S" or an "A" to show if it is an antonym or a synonym for the bold word.

1. Sam is celebrating a **victory**, but his brother is unhappy about a defeat.
2. After years of **captivity**, the bird was given its freedom.
3. "Don't buy cheap shoes," Mom said. "They might be **inexpensive**, but they won't be comfortable."
4. Jorge makes frequent trips to the library, but Mandy **seldom** goes.
5. Some people are generous during trick-or-treat, but Mrs. Dillar is **stingy** with candy.
6. Although she is small, Devin is **courageous**. People admire her because she is so brave.
7. Mrs. Baker said my answer was not exactly **accurate**, but it was not wrong either.
8. Some people are calm before they have to give a speech, but some are **troubled**.
9. At first, the shipwrecked people had hope that they would be rescued, but eventually, they felt **despair**.
10. Mason's cat, Pebbles, is quite **stout**. I wonder how he got so fat?
11. Right now, purple shoes are the **fashion**, but last year, the style was to wear red ones.
12. The train moves **rapidly**, while automobiles move slowly.
13. "Someone should stay after school to help the teacher," I said. "I will **remain** until 4 o'clock."
14. My brother **injured** his shoulder playing football. He hurt it so badly that he had to go to the doctor.
15. Mikey's mom is an **attorney**, and he wants to be a lawyer, too.

© Demco, Inc. 2010

Synonym/Antonym Cards 1

absent (use an antonym)	**factual** (use a synonym)
serious (use an antonym)	**excess** (use a synonym)
poverty (use an antonym)	**accurate** (use a synonym)
permanent (use an antonym)	**irritable** (use a synonym)
private (use an antonym)	**reply** (use a synonym)
gloomy (use an antonym)	**vanish** (use a synonym)
freedom (use an antonym)	**fragile** (use a synonym)
innocent (use an antonym)	**observe** (use a synonym)

© Demco, Inc. 2010

Synonym/Antonym Cards 2

discover (use a synonym)	**deny** (use an antonym)
certain (use an antonym)	**feeble** (use an antonym)
injure (use a synonym)	**complicated** (use an antonym)
common (use a synonym)	**unaware** (use an antonym)
strike (use a synonym)	**perish** (use a synonym)
purchase (use a synonym)	**bitter** (use an antonym)
emotions (use a synonym)	**maximum** (use an antonym)
instantly (use a synonym)	**attractive** (use an antonym)

© Demco, Inc. 2010

Directions: Sentence Sort

Whole Class 

Discuss synonyms with the class, and explain that there are words that mean the same thing, but to varying degrees. Write the following 12 categories on pieces of paper and hang them around the room: Smart, Dumb, Clean, Dirty, Fast, Pretty, Quiet, Ugly, Loud, Fun, Strange, and Normal. Reproduce the Sentence Sort pages on pages 42–45 and cut them apart. Hand out a sentence card to every student, and ask them to read the sentence silently, then stand under the heading for which the bold word is a synonym. When everyone is in place, have each student read his or her sentence out loud and ask the class to decide if the student is under the correct heading.

Individual/Small Group ● /● ●

Write each category heading on an index card. Then, reproduce the Sentence Sort pages and cut them apart. Place the index cards and the sentences in a learning center. Ask students to sort the sentences into the correct heading categories.

Ask students to discuss the sentences that have words for which they did not know the meaning. Encourage them to identify context clues in the sentences that helped them learn the meaning of the word.

Answer Key

SMART: 1, 13, 28, 31
DUMB: 6, 19, 29, 35, 39
CLEAN: 7, 23, 30, 36
DIRTY: 5, 17, 25, 40
FAST: 8, 18, 24
PRETTY: 12, 20, 27, 45
QUIET: 2 , 41, 43, 48
UGLY: 9, 16, 26, 46
LOUD: 10, 21, 34, 47
FUN: 3, 22, 42, 44
STRANGE: 11, 15, 33, 38
NORMAL: 4, 14, 32, 37

© Demco, Inc. 2010

Sentence Sort 1

Some tests are used to find out how **intelligent** a person is.

The audience became **hushed** as the man walked to the microphone to give his speech.

The picnic was **enjoyable** until it started raining.

"Nothing exciting happened," Caleb told his mom. "It was an **ordinary** day."

The lawn chairs were **grimy**, so Dad wiped them off before he let us sit in them.

"That's a **silly** knock-knock joke," Eddie said. "It didn't even make sense!"

Ms. Duggan doesn't like messes, so we can't go out for recess until our desks are **neat**.

The rabbits in our neighborhood are very **swift**—we can never catch them.

This puppy is **plain** compared to its cute brothers and sisters.

Sometimes my family is so **noisy** that I can't concentrate on my homework.

On Crazy Day at school, we like to wear **weird** clothes.

On her wedding day, the princess wore a **dazzling** dress of silk and satin.

© Demco, Inc. 2010

Sentence Sort 2

My cat is so **clever** that she figured out a way to open a closed door.

"The **typical** person checks out three books," said the librarian, "but a few check out many more."

The platypus is an **odd** animal—it has a bill like a duck and fur like a cat.

Molly thought Gino's painting was **hideous** because she did not like the colors he used.

I always wash my little brother's **grubby** hands after he plays in the dirt.

We had just enough time to stop at Grandma's for a **quick** visit on our way to school.

Some people talk slowly, but that does not mean that they are **stupid**—they could be quite smart!

Kayla thinks that puppies are **cute** but that kittens are even more adorable.

Suri was having trouble reading because the sound of the trucks outside was **deafening**.

Roller coaster rides can be **thrilling**, but for some people, the excitement is too much!

The doctor's office should be **spotless** because germs grow best in dirty places.

Speedy animals, like the cheetah, are hard for other animals to catch.

© Demco, Inc. 2010

Sentence Sort 3

After three days of camping in the rain, we were **filthy**, so we took long showers.

"Close the closet door," Mom said. "The mess in there is **unsightly**, and I don't want to see it."

Marlene thought the painting of the castle was **beautiful**, especially the perfect blue sky.

Some people are so **brilliant** that they always know the answer to any question.

If you are **ignorant** about a topic, try reading a book about it—then you will know more.

In between patients, the dentist washes her hands to make sure they are **sanitary**.

The **wise** old man would think about our questions and then answer them carefully and completely.

For a two-year-old child, a temper tantrum is nothing special—it's the **usual** way to behave.

Sometimes kids tease Marcus because his haircut is **different** than other people's normal hairstyles.

We all woke up in the middle of the night because the fire trucks drove by with their **blaring** sirens.

The comedian's jokes were **idiotic**—nobody thought they were funny.

"Will you please **tidy** up the living room?" Wanda asked. "There are papers and books all over the place."

© Demco, Inc. 2010

Sentence Sort 4

Harmony is taller than the **average** four-year-old, but she weighs the same as most kids her age.

The movie had some **bizarre** characters, including a man who carved statues out of cheddar cheese.

My teacher doesn't like it when we waste time with **foolish** chatter.

If you get a cut, you should wash your hands before you touch it. Your hands are **unsanitary** unless you wash them.

If you have a question in class, don't remain **silent**—raise your hand and ask the teacher for help.

"This book was **exciting** to read because the characters had lots of adventures," Dylan said.

After the mother bird fed her babies, they were **still** for awhile, but they soon got noisy again.

We had a **pleasant** time at the party because everyone was nice to us.

My mom bought the yellow car instead of the black one because she thought it was more **attractive**.

Julia bought this hamster because it was so **unattractive** that she thought no one else would want it.

Mr. Jenson has a **booming** voice, so he always makes the announcements at lunch—no one can say they didn't hear him!

When you are birdwatching in the woods, try to be **noiseless** so you won't disturb the animals you are trying to watch.

© Demco, Inc. 2010

Directions: Using Picture Clues

Whole Class ●●●

Reproduce What's Wrong with This Picture? 1 or 2 on page 47 or 48 on a transparency. Explain that there is something in each picture that doesn't fit. Have students identify different things in each picture. Ask them if they see anything that doesn't belong. Have students study the picture and write the object that they think doesn't belong on a slip of paper. Have them also write an object they think would be a good replacement for the wrong object. Collect the papers, sort the answers by popularity, and write the results on the board. Ask students to evaluate all the answers: what context clues do they think led to these responses?

Small Group ●●

After students have worked through What's Wrong with This Picture?, provide paper for them to draw their own pictures with wrong objects. Have them include at least three context clues in each picture. When finished, have them swap with their partners. The partner should decide what is wrong in the picture and come up with an alternative object to replace the wrong object.

Individual ●

Reproduce one of the What's Wrong with This Picture? pages for each student. Have students evaluate the pictures to identify the objects that do not belong. Then, have them write their answers and replacement objects below the pictures. They should also circle at least three things in each picture that helped them figure out which object did not belong. Discuss the activity as a class.

Answer Key

What's Wrong with This Picture? 1 (Page 47)

1. books/lunch trays
2. cat/basketball
3. floor lamp/bride
4. chair/piñata

What's Wrong with This Picture? 2 (Page 48)

1. shoes/hot dogs
2. bucket/telescope
3. roller blades/hiking boots
4. ski poles/paddles

© Demco, Inc. 2010

What's Wrong with This Picture? 1

Name:

Directions: Find the object that doesn't belong in each picture. Write the object on the lines below. Then write what should actually be in the picture.

© Demco, Inc. 2010

What's Wrong with This Picture? 2

Name:____________________________

Directions: Find the object that doesn't belong in each picture. Write the object on the lines below. Then write what should actually be in the picture.

© Demco, Inc. 2010